Pictu

Specific Skill Series

Getting the Main Idea

Richard A. Boning

Fifth Edition

SRA/McGraw-Hill
Columbus, Ohio

Cover, Back Cover, Jonathan Scott/Masterfile

SRA/McGraw-Hill

*A Division of The **McGraw·Hill** Companies*

Send all inquiries to:
   SRA/McGraw-Hill
   8787 Orion Place
   Columbus, OH 43240-4027

ISBN 0-02-687969-7

9 WAL 05

To the Teacher

PURPOSE:

GETTING THE MAIN IDEA is designed to assist pupils in grasping the central thought of a short passage. This skill is not only one of the most important of all major skills, but one which must be developed from the earliest stages.

FOR WHOM:

The skill of GETTING THE MAIN IDEA is developed through a series of books spanning ten levels (Picture, Preparatory, A, B, C, D, E, F, G, H). The Picture Level is for pupils who have not acquired a basic sight vocabulary. The Preparatory Level is for pupils who have a basic sight vocabulary but are not yet ready for the first-grade-level book. Books A through H are appropriate for pupils who can read on levels one through eight, respectively. **The use of the *Specific Skill Series Placement Test* is recommended to determine the appropriate level.**

THE NEW EDITION:

The fifth edition of the *Specific Skill Series* maintains the quality and focus that has distinguished this program for more than 25 years. A key element central to the program's success has been the unique nature of the reading selections. Nonfiction pieces about current topics have been designed to stimulate the interest of students, motivating them to use the comprehension strategies they have learned to further their reading. To keep this important aspect of the program intact, a percentage of the reading selections have been replaced in order to ensure the continued relevance of the subject material.

In addition, a significant percentage of the artwork in the program has been replaced to give the books a contemporary look. The cover photographs are designed to appeal to readers of all ages.

SESSIONS:

Short practice sessions are the most effective. It is desirable to have a practice session every day or every other day, using a few units each session.

SCORING:

Pupils should record their answers on the reproducible worksheets. The worksheets make scoring easier and provide uniform records of the pupils' work. Using worksheets also avoids consuming exercise books.

To the Teacher

It is important for pupils to know how well they are doing. For this reason, units should be scored as soon as they have been completed. Then a discussion can be held in which pupils justify their choices. (The Integrated Language Activities, many of which are open-ended, do not lend themselves to an objective score; thus there are no answer keys for these pages.)

GENERAL INFORMATION ON *GETTING THE MAIN IDEA:*

There are several ways by which teachers can help pupils identify main ideas.

A. **Topic Words:** Pupils tell in a word or two the topic of the paragraph.
B. **Key Question Words:** Pupils learn that questions can begin with special words: *Why, Where, When, How,* and *What.*
C. **Place Clues:** Pupils become aware of paragraph structure. They learn that the main idea is often stated in the first or last sentence.
D. **Space Clues:** Pupils learn that the central thought of a paragraph is not limited to a single sentence, even though it may be stated in one sentence.
E. **Turnabout Clues:** If the main idea is stated in one sentence, pupils learn to change that sentence into a question and see if the whole paragraph answers it.
F. **General and Specific Ideas:** Pupils understand that some words are more general or inclusive than others. Pupils compare sentences to determine which are more inclusive and which are supporting sentences.

SUGGESTED STEPS:

1. Pupils read the passage. (On the Picture Level, they look at the picture.)
2. After reading each passage (or looking at the picture), the readers select its main idea. The choices are on the opposite page (or below the picture/passage, at the Picture, Preparatory, and A levels).

Additional information on using GETTING THE MAIN IDEA with pupils will be found in the **Specific Skill Series Teacher's Manual**.

RELATED MATERIALS:

Specific Skill Series Placement Tests, which enable the teacher to place pupils at their appropriate levels in each skill, are available for the Elementary (Pre-1–6) and Midway (4–8) grade levels.

A picture is about something. Look at page 6. Look at the picture. Think about what the picture shows.

What do you see? Baby birds have their mouths open. The big bird has a worm. These sentences tell about parts that make up the whole picture.

But what is this whole picture about? This sentence tells about the whole picture:

The baby birds want to eat.

A sentence that tells what the picture is mostly about is the **main idea**.

Think of a main idea as being like a tree. A tree has many parts. It has a trunk, roots, leaves, and branches. All these parts together make a whole tree. The word *tree* brings together all these parts, and the main idea of a picture brings together all of *its* parts.

In this book, you will look at pictures. Think about all the things you see in each picture. Ask yourself, "What is the picture mostly about?" Then pick the sentence that tells the main idea of the picture.

What is the main idea?

(A) The baby birds want to play.

(B) The baby birds want to eat.

What is the main idea?

(A) The man has a new hat.

(B) The man is hot.

What is the main idea?

    (A) The girls and boys are playing ball.

    (B) The girls and boys are going home.

What is the main idea?

   (A) The boy has two bikes.

   (B) The boy is riding a bike.

What is the main idea?

(A) The girls are getting wet.

(B) It is not going to rain.

What is the main idea?

(A) **The girl did her work.**

(B) **The girl is reading a book.**

What is the main idea?

(A) The boy is helping his mother.

(B) The boy is eating cake.

What is the main idea?

(A) The girl got a new coat.

(B) Mother is going away.

What is the main idea?

(A) The boy is going to bed.

(B) The boy is making the bed.

What is the main idea?

(A) **The girl is reading.**

(B) **The girl is jumping.**

What is the main idea?

  (A) The man painted a boat.

  (B) The man likes to fish.

What is the main idea?

(A) **The TV is little.**

(B) **The girl is looking at TV.**

A. Exercising Your Skill

Look at the picture of the boy. What is he doing?

Finish the word map below. The main idea is missing in the middle. You can guess the main idea by reading the words in the circles.

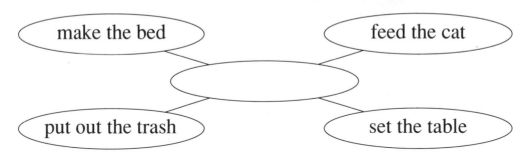

make the bed

feed the cat

put out the trash

set the table

B. Expanding Your Skill

How many steps does it take to do a certain job? Pick one of the circled jobs in Part A. Make that job be the main idea. Under that main idea, write three or four steps that tell how to do that job.

C. Exploring Language

Look at the picture below. On your paper, copy the story that follows. Use your own words to fill in the blanks. Give the story a name that tells the main idea.

Do you ever do chores outside? You can rake the ___, take out the ___, or pick up ___ from the street. You can keep your neighborhood clean.

D. Expressing Yourself

Do one of these things.

1. Do you have jobs to do in your classroom? Make a chart that shows how many times you do each classroom job. At the top of the chart, write a name for the chart.

2. Draw a picture of what your classroom would look like if it never, ever was cleaned up. Write a name on your picture.

What is the main idea?

(A) The girl has two pets.

(B) The dog is eating.

What is the main idea?

(A) **The boy is working.**

(B) **The boy is playing ball.**

What is the main idea?

   (A) The cat wants to get down.

   (B) The cat and the girl are friends.

What is the main idea?

(A) The girl is looking for her dog.

(B) The dog wants something to eat.

What is the main idea?

    (A) The goat is running away.

    (B) The goat is helping the man.

What is the main idea?

(A) The girl is going up.

(B) The girl is getting down.

What is the main idea?

(A) The house is on fire.

(B) Mother is not home.

What is the main idea?

(A) **The girl has a pet.**

(B) **The girl is at a zoo.**

What is the main idea?

   (A) The boy is calling his dog.

   (B) The dog will not come.

What is the main idea?

(A) A cat is in a box.

(B) The children made a train.

29

What is the main idea?

(A) The girls go to bed.

(B) The girls like hot dogs.

What is the main idea?

(A) The boy and girl are playing.

(B) Mother is home.

A. Exercising Your Skill

Look at the picture. Where does the picture take place?

Make believe you are a reporter for your school newspaper. You are going to write a story about the zoo. If you answer these questions about the zoo, you will have the facts, or details, of your story. Pick a name that tells the main idea of the story.

Who visits the zoo?
Where are the animals?
What do people do at the zoo?

B. Expanding Your Skill

Why do people go to the zoo? The main idea of a visit to the zoo is to see the animals. Write the words <u>Zoo Animals</u>. Then list as many animals as you can think of that could live in a zoo.

C. Exploring Language

Draw a picture of your favorite animal at a zoo. Then copy the story that follows on your paper. Use your own words to fill in the blanks. Write a name for your story that tells the main idea.

My favorite zoo animal is the ___ . I like it because it looks so ___ ! I think its favorite food must be ___ . When you see my favorite animal in a zoo, it is usually ___ .

D. Expressing Yourself

Do one of these things.

1. With a friend, pretend that you are planning some zoo space for some polar bears. Write a list of all the things you would need to remember to put into the space. Remember where polar bears live in the wild. Compare your plans with your classmates' plans.

2. Pretend you are a TV reporter. Make up a TV news show that tells about a new zoo that is opening up in your city. Give a name to your show.

What is the main idea?

(A) **The girl is going fast.**

(B) **The girl is going home.**

What is the main idea?

(A) The pig wants to run.

(B) The boy is petting a pig.

What is the main idea?

(A) The girl has a big hat.

(B) The hat is too little.

What is the main idea?

(A) The boy is going fishing.

(B) The boy is falling.

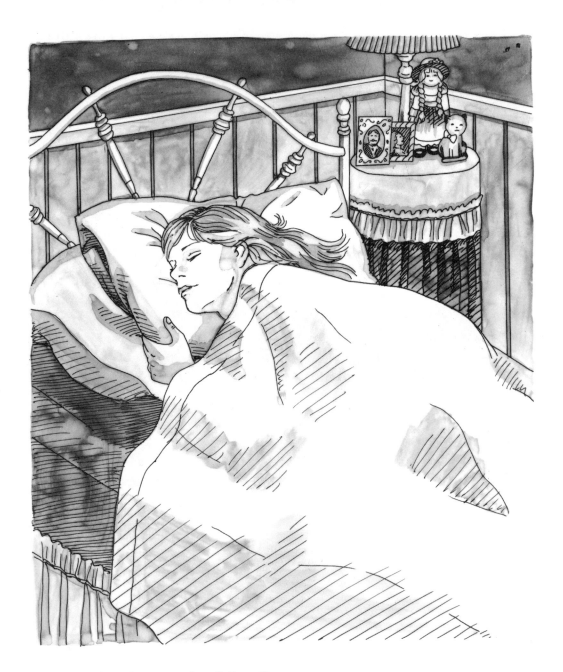

What is the main idea?

(A) The girl is getting up.

(B) The girl is in bed.

What is the main idea?

(A) **The boy is playing with the baby.**

(B) **The baby has a hat.**

What is the main idea?

(A) The girl is talking to her mother.

(B) The girl is eating cake.

What is the main idea?

(A) The boy is looking at the rain.

(B) The boy is working in the rain.

What is the main idea?

(A) The girl can not walk.

(B) The girl is sitting in the sun.

What is the main idea?

(A) No one is in the car.

(B) The ball went into the road.

What is the main idea?

(A) The boy is making a boat.

(B) The boat can go fast.

What is the main idea?

    (A) **The girl sat on a toy.**

    (B) **The girl has a new toy.**

What is the main idea?

(A) The boy is playing a game.

(B) The boy is getting his feet wet.

What is the main idea?

(A) The boy is looking at the sharks.

(B) Sharks are good to eat.

A. Exercising Your Skill

Look at the picture of the girl in the sun. Then read each group of words below the picture. On your own paper, write a good heading that tells the main idea for each group of words.

At the Beach

_____	_____
sand	swim
sun	sail a boat
water	sit in the sun

B. Expanding Your Skill

Share your headings with your classmates. Did you pick the same ideas? Under each heading on your paper, copy the words from the lists above. Then add other words that fit each list.

C. Exploring Language

Listen to the story. Give the story a good name that tells the main idea of the story. Write the name on your paper.

When the weather is hot, many people like to go swimming. Many people cool off in a pool or a lake. Some people go swimming in the ocean, where the water is salty. Other people swim in a river or a creek. If you can't get to any of these places, you can always soak in a cold bathtub!

D. Expressing Yourself

Do one of these things.

1. Write a weather report for your town on the hottest day of the year. Give some ideas on how to cool off in a heat wave.

2. Draw a picture of your favorite place to swim. Put yourself in the picture. Write a sentence to tell about your swimming spot.

What is the main idea?

(A) **The girl can not see the cat.**

(B) **The cat is in the tree.**

What is the main idea?

(A) The boy can not run.

(B) The boy is jumping.

What is the main idea?

   (A) The girl is calling her pet.

   (B) The girl is talking.

What is the main idea?

(A) **The boy is riding.**

(B) **The trees are very little.**

What is the main idea?

(A) The girls are going to work.

(B) The girls are running.

What is the main idea?

(A) **The girl can not play.**

(B) **All the girls are jumping.**

What is the main idea?

(A) The boy is reading to his mother.

(B) Mother has work to do.

What is the main idea?

   (A) **The girl is riding in an airplane.**

   (B) **The girl is painting an airplane.**

What is the main idea?

(A) The goat will not go.

(B) The boy has a pet.

What is the main idea?

   (A) **The man is helping the girl.**

   (B) **The girl is helping the man.**

What is the main idea?

(A) Father likes to ride.

(B) The boy got a new bike.

What is the main idea?

(A) **The girls are playing by the water.**

(B) **The girls are in the water.**

A. Exercising Your Skill

What is the boy in the picture doing?

Copy the word map below. Think about the words in the circles. What are they all about? Write the main idea in the empty circle.

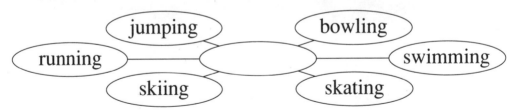

B. Expanding Your Skill

Some sports have lots of jumping. Some sports have no jumping. Pick three sports from the box below that have lots of jumping. Write the sports in a list. Write a heading that tells the main idea of the list.

basketball	soccer	jump rope
hopscotch	swimming	running

C. Exploring Language

The boy in the picture is jumping over a bar. Copy this story about the picture on your paper. Use your own words to fill in the blanks. Give the story a name that tells the main idea.

James is in the jumping contest. He has worked hard to get ready for this day. He wants to ____ higher than he ever has before. He wants to jump the ____ of all. If he jumps high enough, he will break a record! Then he will be the ____ jumper at the school.

D. Expressing Yourself

Do one of these things.

1. Tell your classmates about your favorite sport. Draw a picture of yourself playing the sport. Give the picture a name.

2. Pretend you are a reporter for a newspaper. Write a story about James. Pick a good headline for the story.